YOUNG AMERICA'S MUSIC

VOLUME VII

WOLFGANG AMADEUS MOZART
1756-1791

This brilliant child, born in Austria, was composing and playing the harpsichord at the age of five. He gave recitals at the courts of Austria, Germany, England and France. Handsome, attractive and a genius, he should have been happy but he was beset with disappointments and died young, and in such poverty that his grave is unmarked. In his short life he wrote more works in more forms than any other composer has ever produced.

GIUSEPPE VERDI
1813-1901

He was born and died in Italy, where he had a long and successful life as a composer of operas. Of these *Rigoletto, Il Trovatore* and *Aïda* are probably some of the best known, and many famous arias from them are familiar to devotees of the opera.

YOUNG AMERICA'S MUSIC

Edited by
ALBERT E. WIER

VOLUME VII
PIANO PIECES FROM THE GRAND OPERAS
PIANO PIECES FROM THE LIGHT OPERAS

PIANO

NEW YORK
CHARLES SCRIBNER'S SONS

FOREWORD

The volumes of YOUNG AMERICA'S MUSIC are devoted to musical compositions of every description that not only appeal to the juvenile love of music because of their melodiousness, but will also tend to foster and develop intelligent appreciation of music in later years.

GRAND OPERA SELECTIONS

VOLUME VII conducts the young pianist on a tour through the greatest French, Italian, Russian, German and English grand operas and light operas. In the field of Italian opera we find selections from Verdi's *Aïda*, *Rigoletto* and *Il Trovatore*, Mascagni's *Cavalleria Rusticana*, Ponchielli's *La Gioconda*, Rossini's *William Tell*, Donizetti's *Lucia* and Bellini's *Norma*. English opera is represented by Balfe's *Bohemian Girl* and *Maritana* by William Vincent Wallace; French opera by Bizet's *Carmen*, Gounod's *Faust* and *Romeo and Juliet*, *Mignon* by Thomas, *Le Prophète* by Meyerbeer and Saint-Saëns' *Samson and Delilah*. Two great Russian operas have also been selected: Tschaikowsky's *Eugene Onégin* and Rimsky-Korsakoff's *Sadko*. German opera offers Mozart's *Don Juan* and *Magic Flute*, Weber's *Oberon* and *Der Freischütz*, Humperdinck's *Hansel and Gretel* and two operas by Richard Wagner—*Tannhäuser* and *Lohengrin*. Young people who learn these pieces will appreciate them all the more when they are played on the radio.

LIGHT OPERA SELECTIONS

Some youthful pianists will feel toward grand opera as they do toward piano pieces by classic masters; they prefer melodies from the light operas which they will naturally regard as more tuneful. For this group Volume VII provides a brilliant array of songs arranged for the piano from Italian, German, French, English and Austrian light operas. The English operettas include several written by Gilbert and Sullivan—*The Mikado, The Gondoliers, Patience, H.M.S. Pinafore* and *The Pirates of Penzance*—also Jakobowski's delightful *Erminie*. The German group includes Flotow's *Martha*, Nessler's *Trumpeter of Säkkingen* and Millocker's *Beggar Student;* from France come Planquette's *Chimes of Normandy*, Offenbach's *Tales of Hoffmann*, Auber's *Fra Diavolo* and Audran's *Olivette*. Modern Austrian operettas are represented by Franz Lehar's *Merry Widow,* and Oscar Straus's *The Waltz Dream;* all of these melodies will delight the young pianist.

YOUNG AMERICA'S MUSIC

VOLUME VII

Piano Pieces from the Grand Operas
Piano Pieces from the Light Operas

CLASSIFIED INDEX

Piano Pieces from the Grand Operas

Piano Pieces from the Light Operas

YOUNG AMERICA'S MUSIC

VOLUME VII
Piano Pieces from the Grand Operas
Piano Pieces from the Light Operas

TITLE INDEX

ORFEO
Andante

C.W. von Gluck

MARTHA

Ah, So Pure

Fr. von Flotow

Allegro moderato

FAUST
Soldiers' March

Ch. Gounod

Tempo di Marcia

FAUST
Lovely Flowers, I Pray

Ch. Gounod

Allegro agitato

THE BOHEMIAN GIRL
When Other Lips And Other Hearts

M. W. Balfe

THE BOHEMIAN GIRL
The Heart Bowed Down

M.W. Balfe

RIGOLETTO
La Donna é Mobile

G. Verdi

RIGOLETTO
Quartet

G. Verdi

CARMEN
Habanera

G. Bizet

CARMEN
Toreador Song

Allegro moderato

G. Bizet

L'ECLAIR
Call Me Thine Own

J. Halévy

EUGENE ONÉGIN

Waltz Movement

P. Tschaikowsky

Tempo di Valse

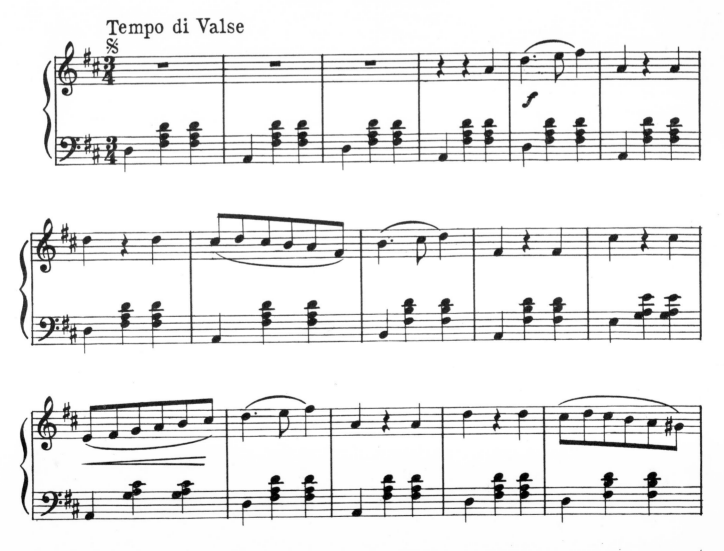

D.S. % al Fine

LA GIOCONDA

Dance of the Hours

A. Ponchielli

THE MAGIC FLUTE
The Birdcharmer's Song

W. A. Mozart

CAVALLERIA RUSTICANA
Intermezzo

P. Mascagni

Andante sostenuto

DON JUAN
Duet

W. A. Mozart

SAMSON AND DELILAH
My Heart at thy Sweet Voice

C. Saint-Saëns

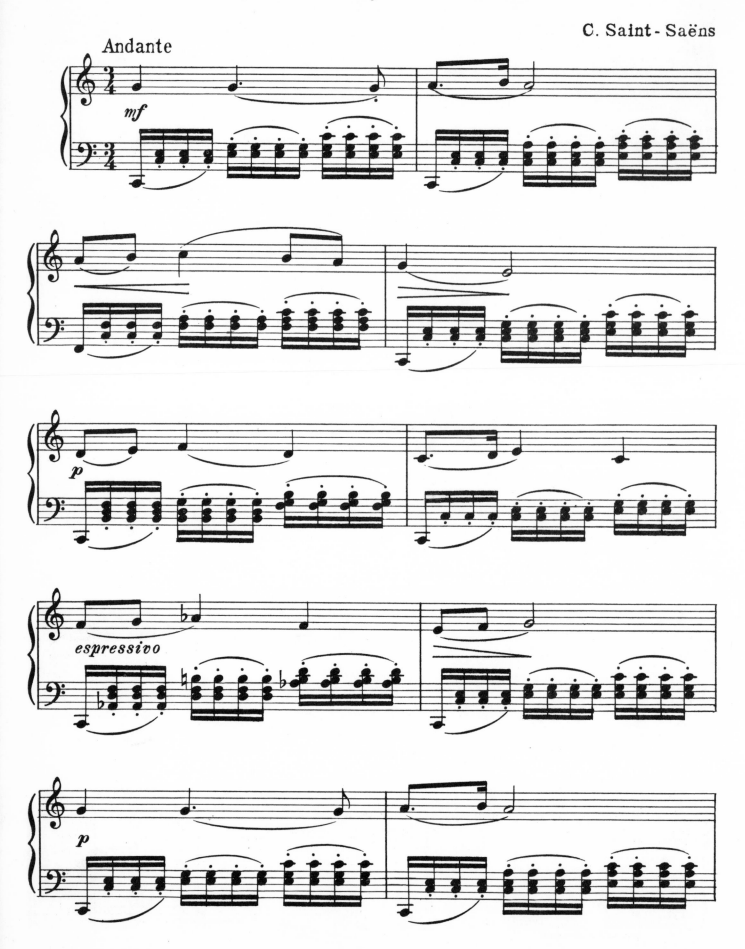

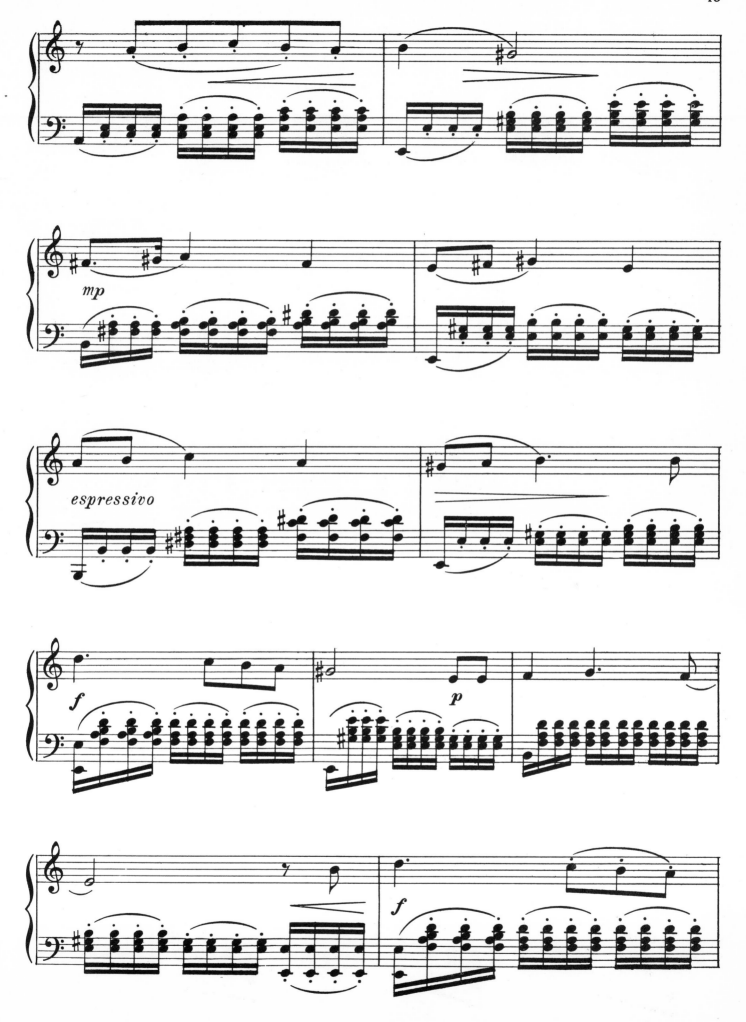

SADKO
Song of India

N. Rimsky-Korsakow

AÏDA
Triumphal March

G. Verdi

THE BARBER OF SEVILLE
Waltz Song

G. Rossini

THE BOHEMIAN GIRL
I Dreamt that I Dwelt in Marble Halls

M. W. Balfe

LUCIA DI LAMMERMOOR
Sextette

G. Donizetti

MARITANA
In Happy Moments

G.V. Wallace

IL TROVATORE

Soldiers' Chorus

G. Verdi

Allegro moderato e maestoso

IL TROVATORE
Anvil Chorus

G. Verdi

Allegro maestoso

IL TROVATORE
Miserere

G. Verdi

Andante sostenuto

IL TROVATORE
Home To Our Mountains

G. Verdi

TANNHÄUSER
Grand March

Richard Wagner

Allegro Maestoso

MIGNON
Entr'acte - Gavotte

A. Thomas

ORFEO
I Have Lost My Eurydice

C. W. von Gluck

DAUGHTER OF THE REGIMENT
Rataplan

G. Donizetti

Allegro con spirito

ROMEO AND JULIET

Waltz Song

Ch. Gounod

Tempo di Valse

TALES OF HOFFMAN
Barcarolle

J. Offenbach

DER FREISCHÜTZ
Prayer

C. M. von Weber

HANSEL AND GRETEL
Evening Prayer

E. Humperdinck

93

TANNHÄUSER
The Evening Star

Rich. Wagner

TANNHÄUSER

Pilgrim Chorus

Rich. Wagner

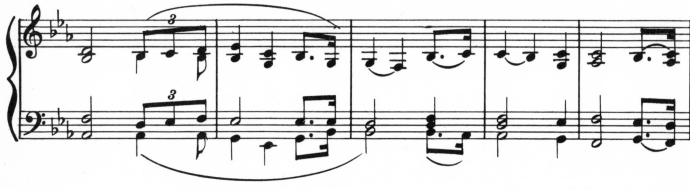

COPPELIA
Valse Lente

L. Delibes

Tempo di Valse lente

DON JUAN

Minuet

W. A. Mozart

Moderato

OBERON
Song of the Mermaids

C. M. von Weber

Andante con moto

LE PROPHÉTE
Coronation March

G. Meyerbeer

Maestoso

D. C. al Fine

LOHENGRIN

Bridal Chorus

Rich. Wagner

Andante

FAUST
Ballet Waltz

Ch. Gounod.

MARTHA
Last Rose of Summer

Fr. von Flotow

Larghetto

DER FREISCHÜTZ

Huntsmen's Chorus

C. M. Von Weber.

Allegretto

NORMA

Grand March

Vincenzo Bellini

Tempo di Marcia

staccato il basso

staccato il basso

WILLIAM TELL
Finale to Overture

G. Rossini

THE MIKADO

Arthur Sullivan

Allegro (The Flowers That Bloom in the Spring)

(The Wandering Minstrel)

Andante (Tit-Willow)

Allegretto grazioso
(Three little maids from school)

ERMINIE

Lullaby

E. Jakobowski

H.M.S. PINAFORE
I'm Called Little Buttercup

Arthur Sullivan

Allegretto

THE CHIMES OF NORMANDY

R. PLANQUETTE

Tempo di Valse (Waltz Song)

Allegro

Andantino (Legend of the Bell)

OLIVETTE
The Torpedo and The Whale

E. Audran

THE MASCOT
The Gobble Duet

E. AUDRAN

THE TRUMPETER OF SAKKINGEN
It Was Not So To Be

V. Nessler

THE BEGGAR STUDENT
Waltz Song

K. Millocker

THE GONDOLIERS

Courtier Song

A. Sullivan

Tempo di Gavotte

THE PIRATES OF PENZANCE
March of the Pirates

A. Sullivan

Allegro marcia

THE QUEEN'S LACE HANDKERCHIEF
The Truffle Song

Joh. Strauss

Tempo di Valse

THE WALTZ DREAM
Viennese Waltz

Oscar Straus

Tempo di Valse Lente

THE WALTZ DREAM
Entr'acte-Gavotte

Allegretto grazioso

Oscar Straus

THE MERRY WIDOW
Vilia Song

Franz Lehar

Andantino

The Grand Duchess
Regimental Song

J. Offenbach

Allegro marcato

Patience
The Magnet Song

Arthur Sullivan

FRA DIAVOLO
On Yonder Rock Reclining

D. F. Auber

Allegretto

THE QUEEN'S LACE HANDKERCHIEF
Wild Rose Song

Joh. Strauss

THE TYROLEAN
Nightingale Song

Carl Zoeller

OLIVETTE
Laughing Song

E. Audran

Tempo di Valse

Ha! ha! ha! ha! ha! ha! ha! ha! ha!

Ha! ha! ha! ha! ha! ha! ha! ha! ha!